786.48

WYTHALL

Please return/renew this item by the last date shown

worcestershire
countycouncil
Cultural Services

The Joy of Movie Music

Arranged by Stephen Duro.

786.48 JOY

Yorktown Music Press / Music Sales Limited

London / New York / Paris / Sydney / Copenhagen / Madrid / Tokyo

Exclusive Distributors:
Music Sales Limited
8/9 Frith Street, London W1D 3JB, England.
Music Sales Pty Limited
120 Rothschild Avenue, Rosebery, NSW 2018, Australia.

Order No. AM963281
ISBN 0-7119-8088-8
This book © Copyright 2000 by Yorktown Music Press / Music Sales Limited

Compiled by Nick Crispin.
Cover illustration by Stuart Briers.
Music arranged by Stephen Duro.
Music processed by Allegro Reproductions.

Music Sales' complete catalogue describes thousands of titles and
is available in full colour sections by subject, direct from Music Sales Limited.
Please state your areas of interest and send a cheque/postal order for £1.50 for postage to:
Music Sales Limited, Newmarket Road, Bury St. Edmunds, Suffolk IP33 3YB.

Your Guarantee of Quality:
As publishers, we strive to produce every book to the highest commercial standards.
The music has been freshly engraved and the book has been carefully designed to minimise
awkward page turns and to make playing from it a real pleasure.
Particular care has been given to specifying acid-free, neutral-sized paper made from
pulps which have not been elemental chlorine bleached.
This pulp is from farmed sustainable forests and was produced with special regard for the environment.
Throughout, the printing and binding have been planned to ensure a sturdy,
attractive publication which should give years of enjoyment.
If your copy fails to meet our high standards, please inform us and we will gladly replace it.

Printed in the United Kingdom by
Caligraving Limited, Thetford, Norfolk.

www.musicsales.com

Platoon
(Adagio For Strings Op. 11)

By Samuel Barber

Molto Adagio ♩ = c.45

4

Casablanca
(As Time Goes By)

By Herman Hupfeld

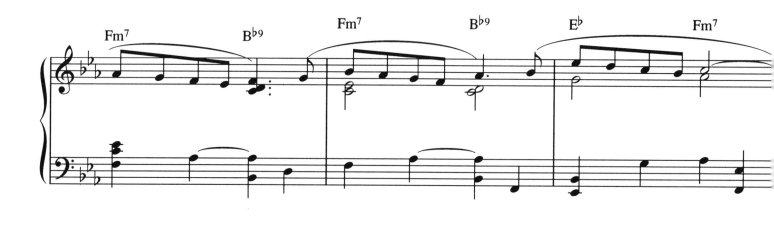

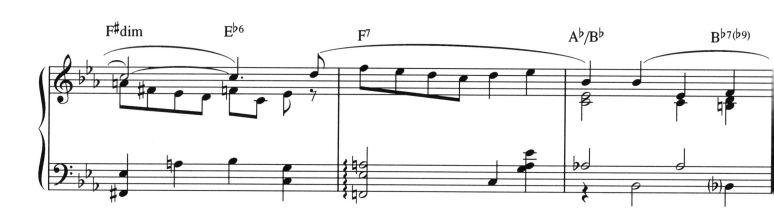

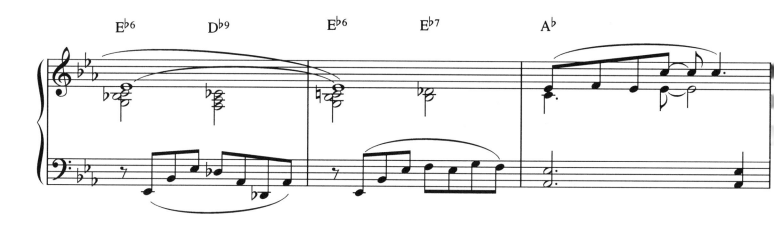

11

American Beauty
(Theme)

By Thomas Newman

Moderately

(con Ped.)

Romeo And Juliet
(Love Theme)

By Nino Rota

Slow and expressive

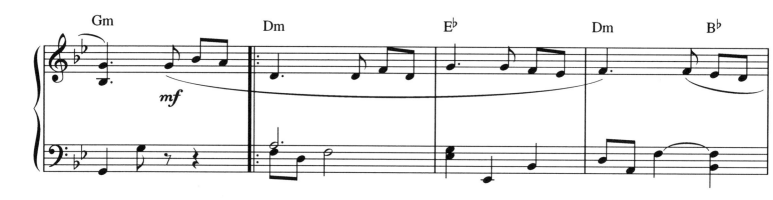

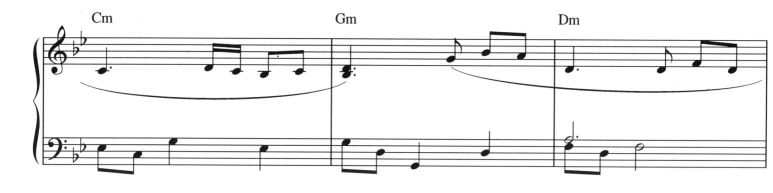

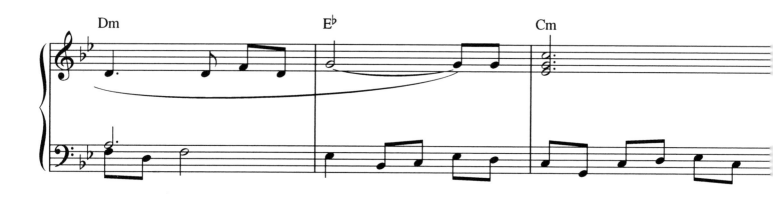

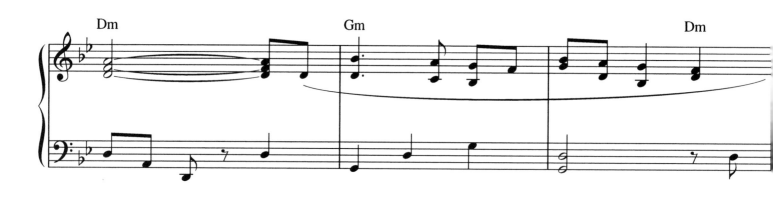

Breakfast At Tiffany's
(Theme)

By Henry Mancini

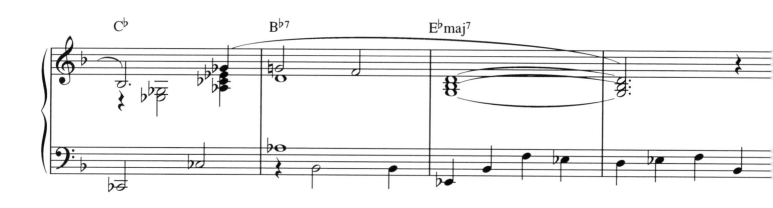

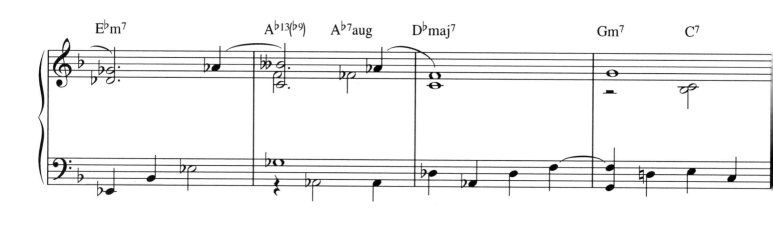

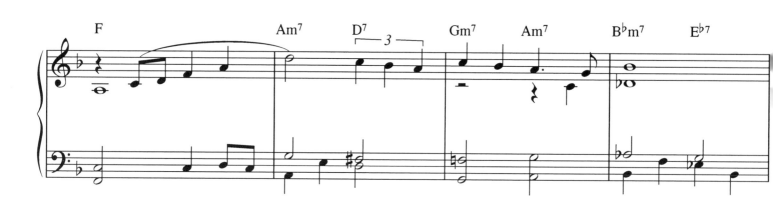

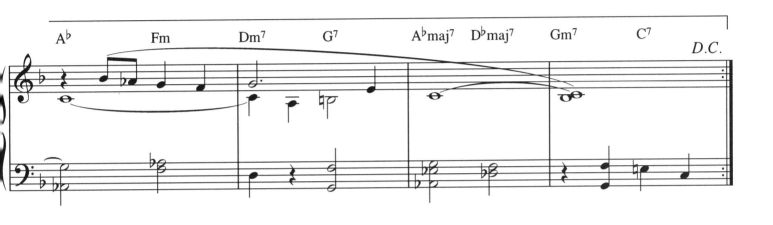

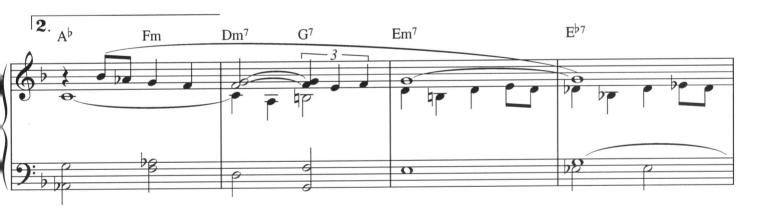

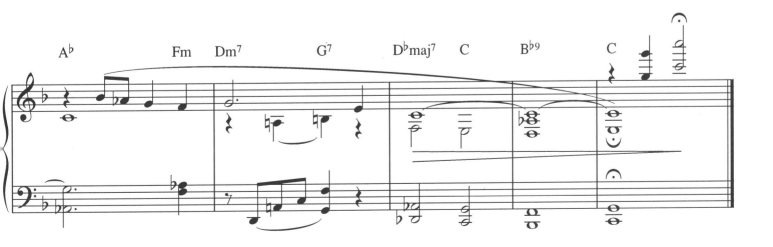

Forrest Gump
(Main Title: Feather Theme)

By Alan Silvestri

(lightly)

22

Local Hero
(Going Home)

By Mark Knopfler

26

Jean De Florette
(Theme)

By Jean-Claude Petit

Lawrence Of Arabia
(Theme)

By Maurice Jarre

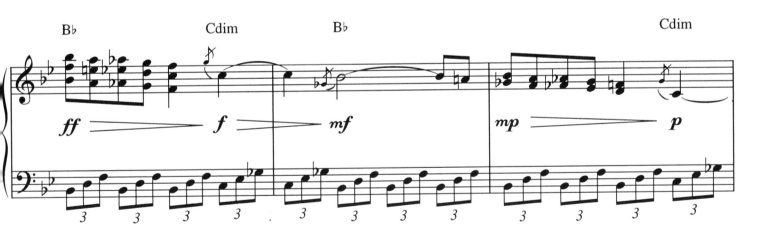

33

Cinema Paradiso
(Love Theme)

By Ennio Morricone & Andrea Morricone

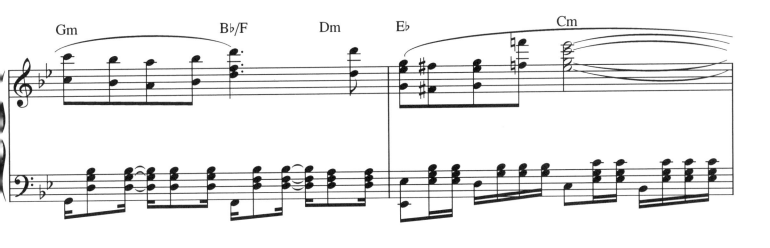

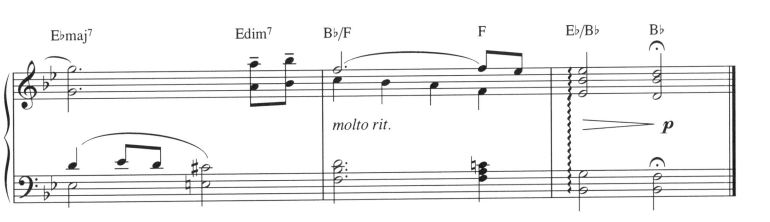

The English Patient
(The English Patient/Rupert Bear)

By Gabriel Yared

Plaintively - not too fast

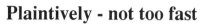

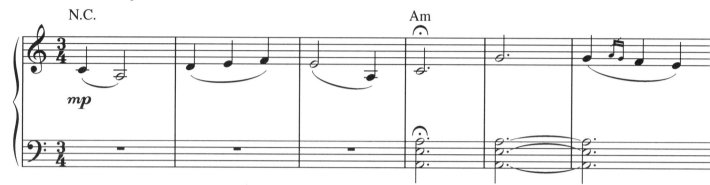

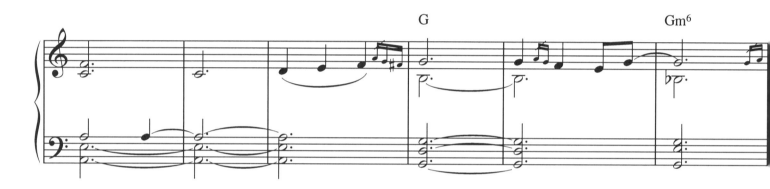

Reflectively (♩ = ♪)

Gone With The Wind
(Tara Theme)

By Max Steiner

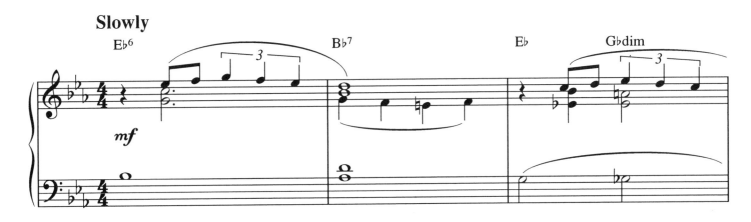

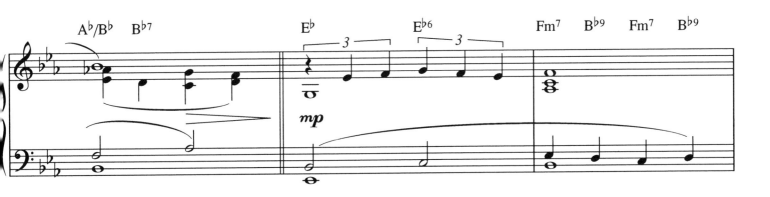

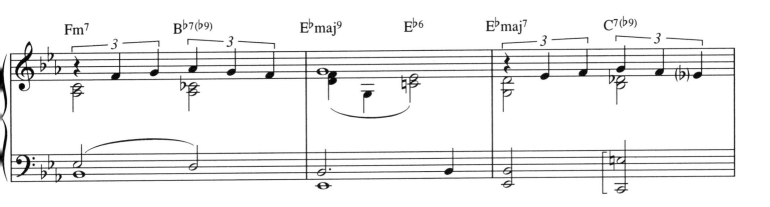

43

Schindler's List
(Theme)

By John Williams

Expressively

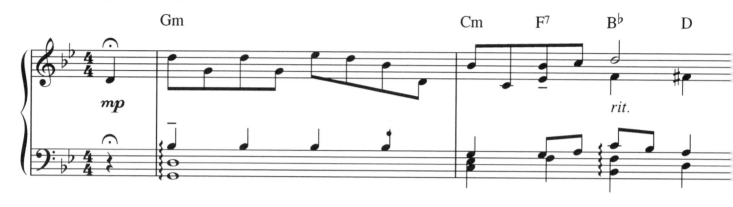

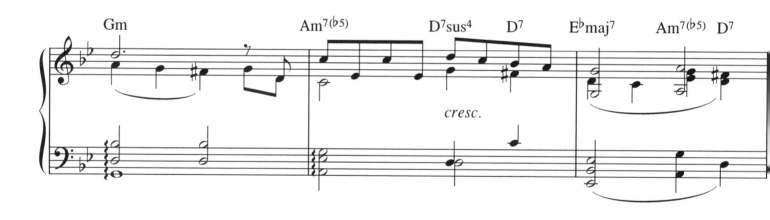

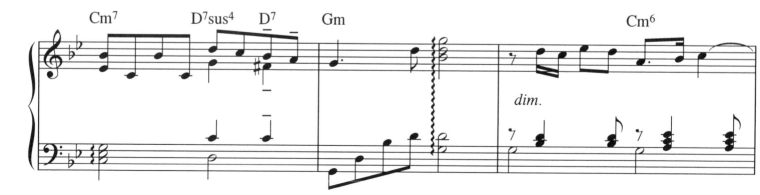

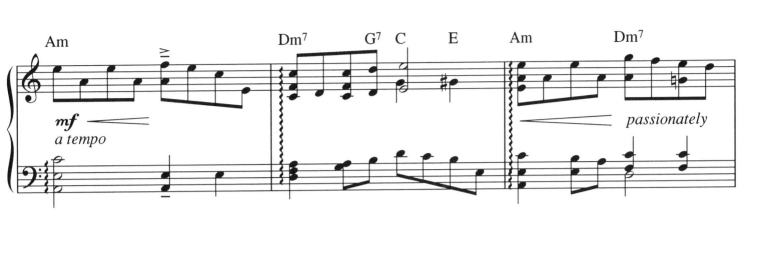

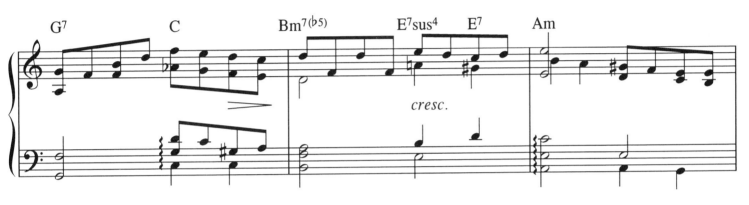

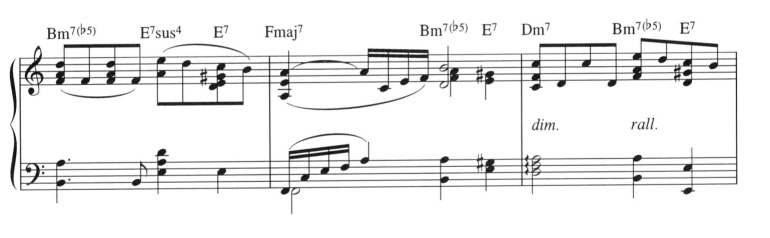

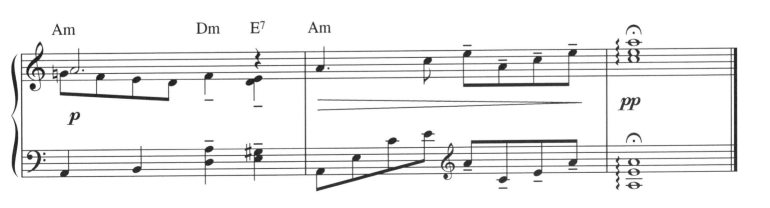

Shakespeare In Love
(The Beginning Of The Partnership)

By Stephen Warbeck

49

The Piano
(The Heart Asks Pleasure First:
The Promise/The Sacrifice)

By Michael Nyman

Vertigo
(Scene D'Amour)

By Bernard Herrmann

Moderately with expression

58

Dances With Wolves
(The John Dunbar Theme)

By John Barry

More Great Music from the Silver Screen

Check out these other selected film titles for solo piano...

Aladdin: Piano Solos

Seven great Disney songs including 'Arabian Nights', 'One Jump Ahead' and 'A Whole New World'.
Order No. HLD00292018 (Easy piano edition with full-colour illustrations from the film also available: Order No. HLD00222555)

Jane Austen: The Music

Solo piano arrangements of music from Sense And Sensibility and Pride And Prejudice.
Order No. AM944592

Beauty And The Beast: Easy Piano

Easy piano arrangements of songs from the popular Disney film, complete with lyrics and chord symbols.
Order No. HLD00110003

Fantasia: Piano Solos

An outstanding matching folio to the Disney landmark movie. Includes arrangements of 15 famous classical pieces as well as full-colour illustrations and six pages of background text about the movie.
Order No. HLD00292006
(Easy piano edition also available: Order No. HLD00490553)

Film Themes Of The Nineties

Music from seven top movie scores of the Nineties specially arranged for solo piano by Jack Long. Includes 'The English Patient', 'Mission: Impossible', 'The Nightmare Before Christmas', 'Schindler's List', 'Sense And Sensibility', 'The Silence Of The Lambs' and 'Toy Story'.
Order No. AM952897

Film Themes Piano Solos

Full piano solo arrangements by Cyril Ornadel of 20 classic film themes. Includes 'Chariots Of Fire', 'Lawrence Of Arabia' and 'Star Wars'.
Order No. AM90204

Selections From Forrest Gump

Twenty-two songs from the movie, arranged for easy piano with lyrics and chord symbols.
Order No. AM938091

I Can Play That! Film Themes

The easiest ever piano arrangements of 13 screen hits, including 'How Deep Is Your Love', 'GoldenEye', 'Circle Of Life' and 'Kiss From A Rose'.
Order No. AM936947

It's Easy To Play Movie Music

Simplified piano arrangements of 19 popular film and TV themes. Screen hits include 'Big Spender', 'Eternally' and 'Over The Rainbow'.
Order No. AM953865

The Lion King: Piano Solos

Seven songs from the movie including 'Circle Of Life', 'This Land', 'Can You Feel The Love Tonight' and 'Be Prepared'.
Order No. HLD00292060

Michael Nyman: The Piano

Original compositions for solo piano from the award-winning film. Play along with the music using the Midi Disk or just listen to the performance by Jane Jackson.
Order Nos. CH60871 (Book only), OM23495 (Disk only), CH61065 (Book and Disk).

The Music Of Michel Legrand

Sixteen outstanding melodies by France's leading film composer arranged as piano solos. Includes 'The Windmills Of Your Mind', and 'The Summer Knows'.
Order No. AM25727

Oliver! Easy Piano

Twelve songs arranged for easy piano with lyrics. Includes 'Oom-Pah-Pah', 'Where Is Love?' and 'Pick A Pocket Or Two'.
Order No. LK56187

Pocahontas: Easy Piano

Beautiful full-colour illustrations and easy piano arrangements from the popular Disney film.
Order No. HLD00316002

Rodgers And Hammerstein Anthology

Thirty-nine of their greatest songs arranged for easy piano, including 'Climb Ev'ry Mountain', 'Getting To Know You', 'Some Enchanted Evening' 'Edelweiss', and 'You'll Never Walk Alone'.
Order No. HLW00366008

Schindler's List: Piano Solos

Thought provoking music by John Williams from the film.
Order No. AM92669

All these superb music books are available from good music retailers, or in case of difficulty, contact the address below.
Music Sales has many more titles featuring selections from the world's top films, stage shows and TV series. For an illustrated copy of the latest Piano catalogue, please send a cheque/postal order for £1.50 for postage to:
Music Sales Limited, Newmarket Road, Bury St. Edmunds, Suffolk IP33 3YB.
Telephone 01284 725725; Fax 01284 702592.

www.musicsales.com